SAILING WITH PAROS
Our Beautiful World

by Yaeko Koizumi Knaus

DORRANCE
PUBLISHING CO
EST. 1920
PITTSBURGH, PENNSYLVANIA 15238

Dorrance Publishing Co
585 Alpha Drive
Pittsburgh, PA 15238
Visit our website at *www.dorrancebookstore.com*

ISBN: 979-8-89027-056-6
eISBN: 979-8-89027-554-7

For the joy of sailing, introduced by my husband Mark and his beloved boat Paros.

For the love of teaching languages, a life work of Dr. Ben Clark.

For the confidence given me to publish this poem by my former principal Dr. Marc Biunno.

Sailing

with

Paros

Our Beautiful World
Written and Illustrated by
Yaeko Koizumi Knaus

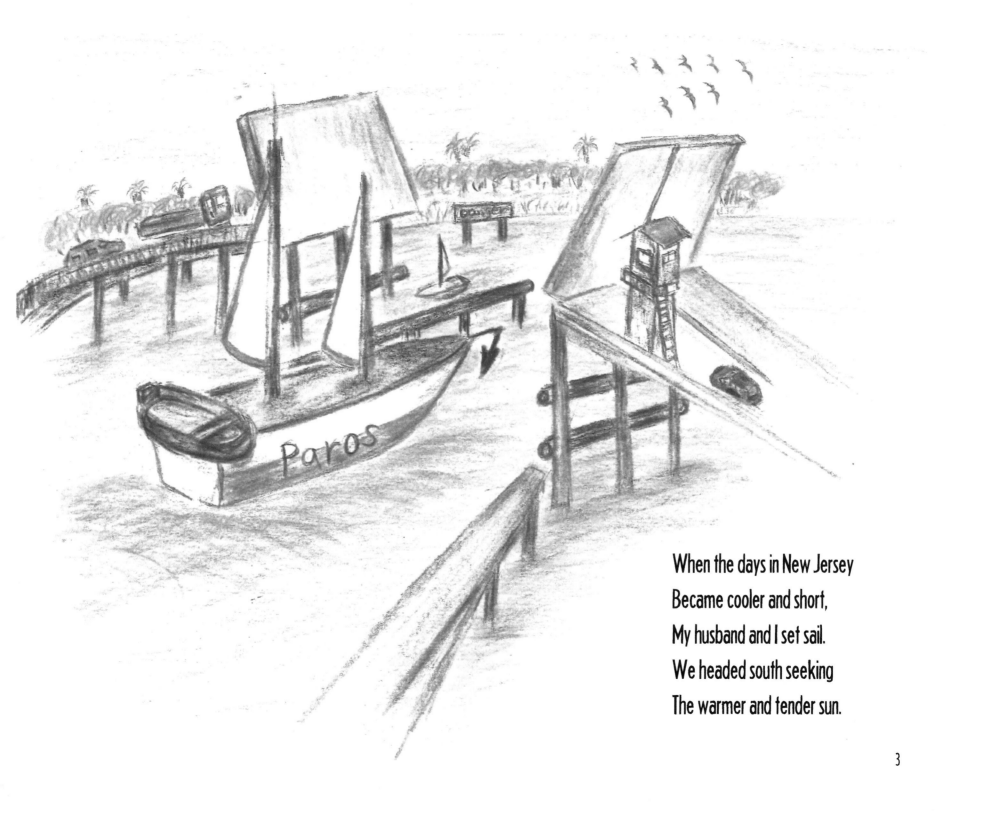

When the days in New Jersey
Became cooler and short,
My husband and I set sail.
We headed south seeking
The warmer and tender sun.

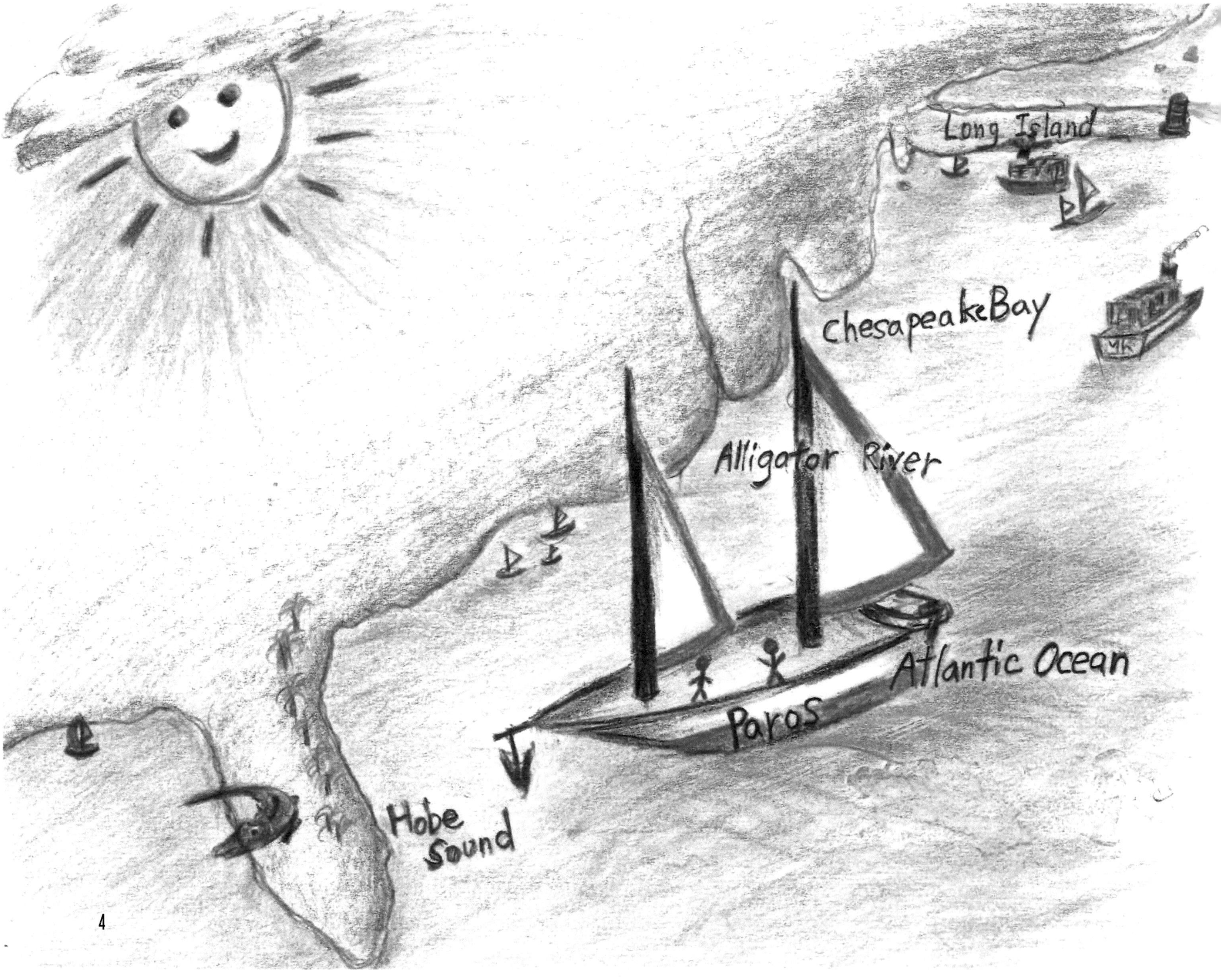

Long Island

ChesapeakeBay

Alligator River

Atlantic Ocean

Paros

Hobe
Sound

4

On the Atlantic Ocean we sailed south,
Through the Chesapeake Bay we glid,
Down the Alligator River we floated,
And up the Hobe Sound we coasted.

6

We loved watching the beautiful bright yellow sky
When the morning sun rose up.
We were elated to see the vivid gorgeous red sky
When the evening sun set down.

We saw a school of blue dolphins
Riding the waves of our sail boat,
And we witnessed the beautiful wild horses
Feeding on the Cumberland Island beach.

A keen eyed bald eagle watched our way
From a branch of a high tree top,
While friendly cormorants
Hung out on the mile markers.
Along the green marshlands,
White pelicans flew low
Gliding over the waveless water.

On the majestic Atlantic Ocean,

We were so excited

To ride the big bouncy waves,

Phew, how exhausting!

So at night, we lowered our anchor

In a calm quiet cove to rest.

14

Our earth is blue,
Our earth is green,
Our earth is sometimes yellow or red,
Beautiful pink? Of course.

Our world is colorful and indeed beautiful.

It makes me happy and gives me joy.

But, to my deepest disappointment,

I saw the blackish murky water

Toward the mouth of a long river.

I saw the worn out plastic bags

Floating in a busy bay.

When I passed by a paper mill,
I saw the smoke stacks puffing and huffing.
I sadly smelled the awful fumes.
How could it happen?
I was furious and I felt sad
Because they are the results of
Numerous heartless human acts.

Can you imagine the dreadful days
The dark depressing sun rises
Beyond the gray dirty smog?
How would you feel
If you can't swim in the ocean
Because the water is not clean enough?

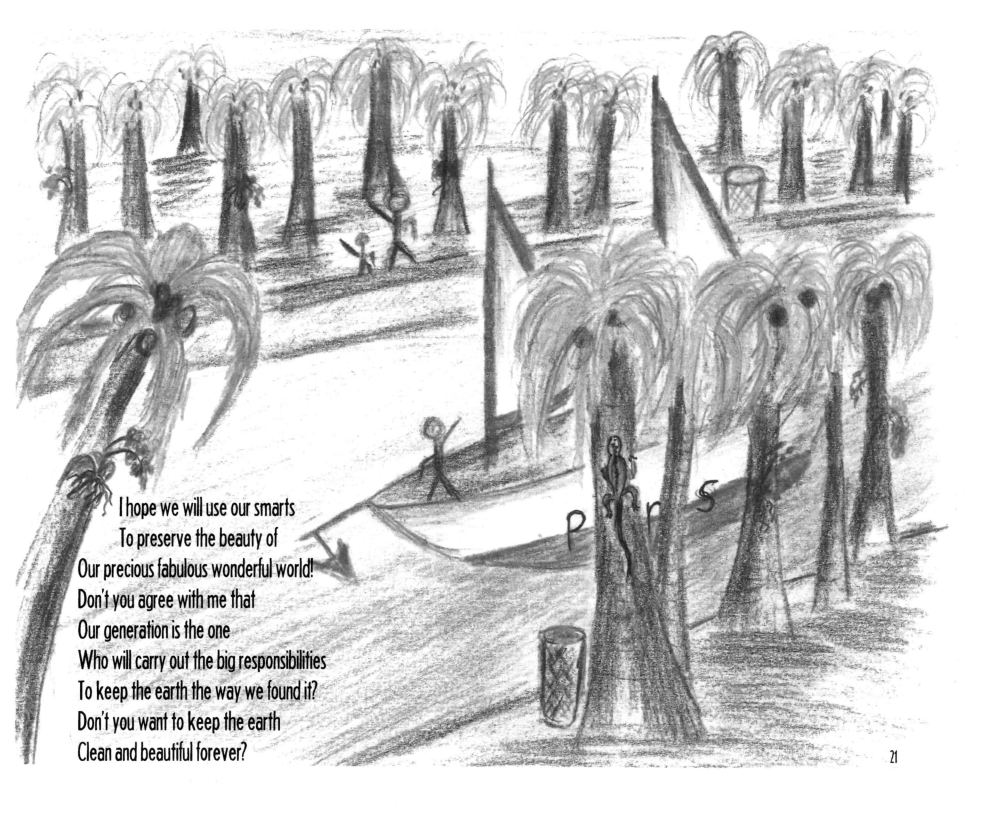

I hope we will use our smarts
    To preserve the beauty of
Our precious fabulous wonderful world!
Don't you agree with me that
Our generation is the one
Who will carry out the big responsibilities
To keep the earth the way we found it?
Don't you want to keep the earth
Clean and beautiful forever?

21

Paros

22

My husband and I drink our coffee on our boat
When the warm morning sun rises.

Carpe Diem, we seize the day
With our adult drinks in hands
When the coolest looking evening sun sets.
We, the sailors, particularly love the red evening sky
Because that is a promise from the sun
Saying that tomorrow will bring another sunny day.

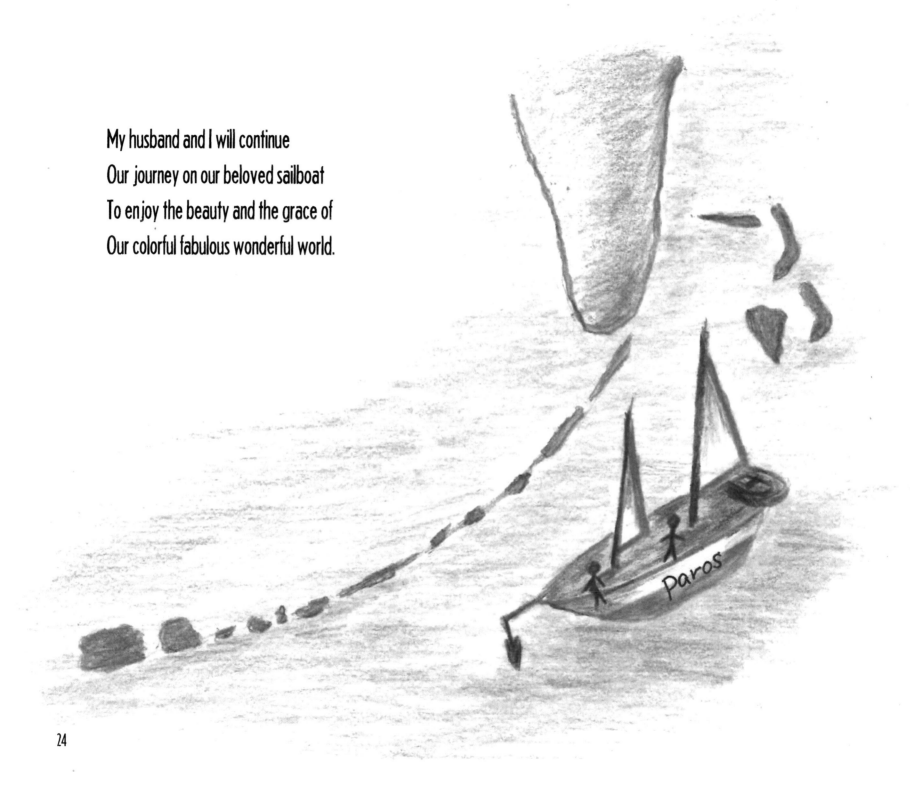

My husband and I will continue
Our journey on our beloved sailboat
To enjoy the beauty and the grace of
Our colorful fabulous wonderful world.

I hope you will do the same someday,
Or whenever you have a lucky chance.
I promise you with all my heart
You will love it as much as I do.

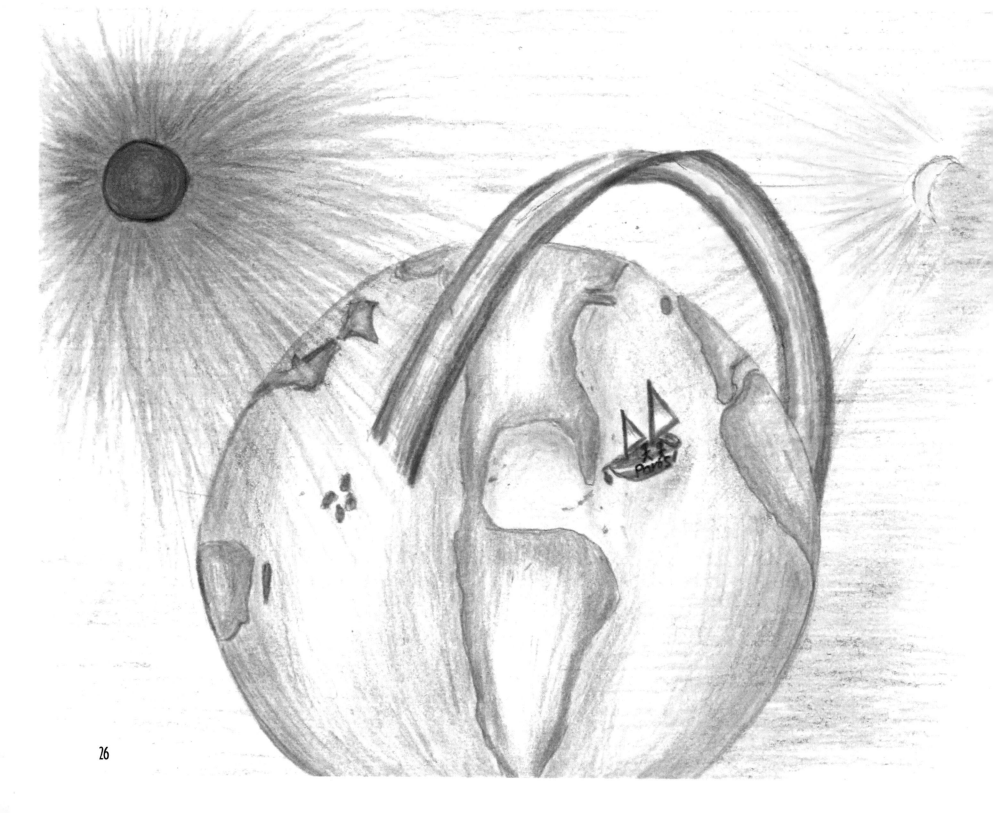

Our world is a very special beautiful place,

It is a masterpiece of all,

Painted with the colors of the rainbow.

Printed in the USA
CPSIA information can be obtained
at www.ICGtesting.com
CBHW042105130424

6791CB00004B/9